The Sic

My bear is not well.
She is sick.

2

I put a bandage on her.
I put her in her bed.

3

I say to Aunt Rose,
"My bear is sick."

4

"Let me look at her,"
says Aunt Rose.

Aunt Rose gets a needle
and some yarn.

Stitch, stitch, stitch.

"Your bear is not sick,"
says Aunt Rose.
"Look! Your bear is well."